Treble Recorder *from the* Beginning

Concert Pieces

With eight duets

John Pitts

This collection of 31 pieces offers treble recorder players a wealth of material to play and enjoy, whether in concert or at home, solo or in a group. Eight optional duets for two trebles are included.

The wide range of repertoire varies from classical favourites by Purcell, Handel, Mozart and Bizet, to 'showstoppers' from *The Lion King*, *Beauty And The Beast* and *Les Misérables*, as well as music by Lloyd Webber. English, Irish, Manx and Russian folksongs rub shoulders with Latin-American dances such as the tango, beguine and samba, along with spirituals, 'blues', ragtime and original pieces by myself.

All the items are carefully graded, and the range of required notes increases steadily, as indicated in the contents list of the books. But the desire to learn a particular piece and play it 'in concert' will always provide the incentive to master any new note that stands in the way! At the start of the book it is expected that the players will have learnt the first eight notes in *Treble Recorder from the Beginning*, which is in the author's widely popular teaching scheme.

The eight duets are all marked 'Solo or Duet'. In each of these the main tune is written in the top part all the way through, so can be played solo. But when played as a duet, the players are directed to change parts at the rehearsal letters so that the musical interest is divided equally between the two parts and both players have equal opportunity to 'shine'.

Both books include guitar chord symbols, and the Latin-American dances usually have suggestions for use of percussion instruments. Where space allows there are comments about the music, but these are more usually found in the Teacher's Book which includes piano accompaniments for all the pieces, as well as some additional pitched/unpitched percussion parts.

I hope you will enjoy playing from this book, and meeting the challenges presented by the wide variety of musical forms and styles.

John Pitts 2006

Chester Music
part of The Music Sales Group
London/New York/Paris/Sydney/Copenhagen/Belin/Madrid/Tokyo

Published by
Chester Music
8/9 Frith Street, London W1D 3JB

Exclusive Distributors:
Music Sales Limited
8/9 Frith Street,
London W1D 3JB, UK.
Music Sales Pty Limited
120 Rothschild Avenue,
Rosebery, NSW 2018, Australia.

Arranging and engraving supplied by Camden Music.
Edited by Ann Farmer
Printed in the EU.

Your Guarantee of Quality
As publishers, we strive to produce every book to the highest commercial standards.
The music has been freshly engraved and the book has been carefully designed to
minimise awkward page turns and to make playing from it a real pleasure.
Throughout, the printing and binding have been planned to ensure a sturdy,
attractive publication which should give years of enjoyment.
If your copy fails to meet our high standards, please inform us and we will gladly replace it.

www.musicsales.com

Contents

Notes listed as included do not necessarily appear often in a piece. Some may occur only once or twice! It is best to assess each item individually.

* For more confident players there are extra audio tracks for eight of the pieces in the CD edition of this book. In these, the same accompaniment is played without the melody.

On My Own from 'Les Miserables'

Music by Claude-Michel Schönberg, arr. John Pitts
Original Lyrics by Alain Boublil & Jean-Marc Natel
English Lyrics by Herbert Kretzmer, Trevor Nunn & John Caird

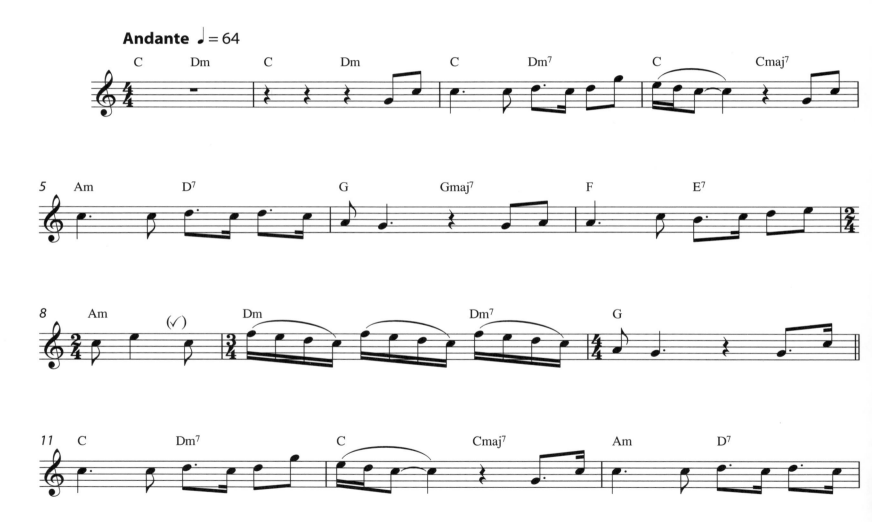

O Waly Waly (English)

Traditional, arr. John Pitts

La Jesucita (Mexican)

Traditional, arr. John Pitts

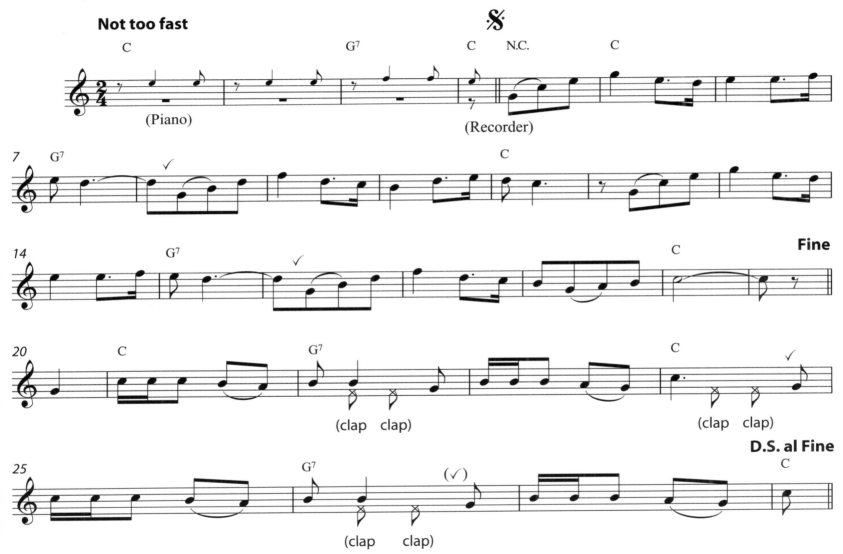

Tango Chacabuco

Music by John Pitts

The **tango** is a Latin-American dance from Argentina, with a catchy rhythm. It began around 1900 in Buenos Aires, the capital city. There is more information about the tango in the Teacher's Book.

Rigaudon (Chédeville)

French Traditional, arr. John Pitts

Solo or Duet The tune is written in the top part all the way through, so can be played solo. When played as a duet the players can change parts for the repeat at the end of each section.

The **Rigaudon** was a French dance, popular at the court of Louis XIV (1645–1715). An early English version was the *Rigadoon* by Henry Purcell (1659–1695). Some modern composers such as Grieg and Ravel have included the *Rigaudon* in their suites (collections of instrumental dance movements).

Can You Feel The Love Tonight?

from Walt Disney Pictures' 'The Lion King'

Words by Tim Rice & Music by Elton John, arr. John Pitts

(Chorus)

molto rit.

Swing Low, Sweet Chariot

American Spiritual

Traditional, arr. John Pitts

The Teacher's Book includes information about American spirituals.

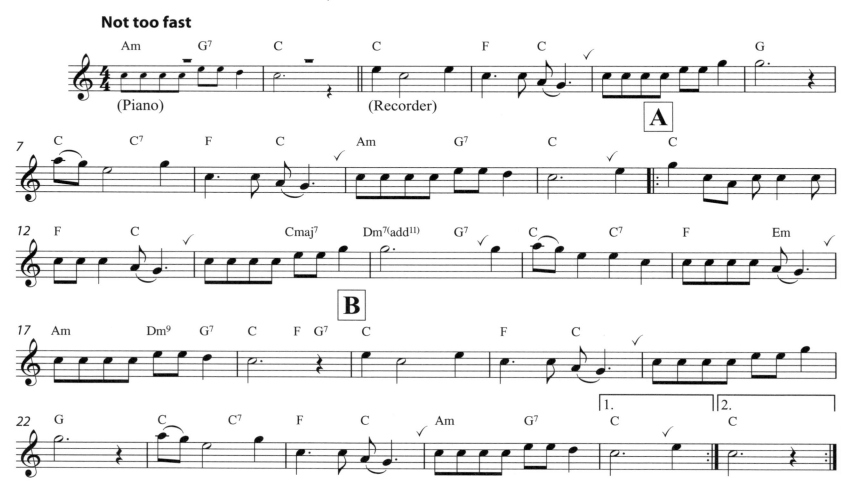

Kalinka (Russian)

Traditional, arr. John Pitts

CD Edition: When playing with the CD hold the pause notes for a length of two counts each, so you know when to move on.

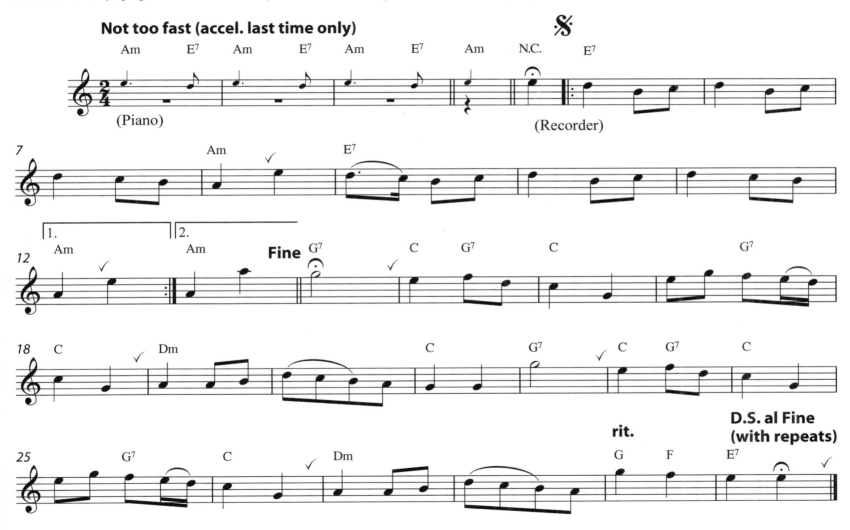

Cascadura Beguine

Music by John Pitts

There is another **beguine** on page 30, with suggestions for some rhythm accompaniments to play.

Tango Las Plumas

Music by John Pitts

Duet or Solo The tune is written in the top part all the way through, so can be played solo. When played as a duet the players can change parts at [A] and back again at the **D.S.**, so that each plays some of the main tune.

Gavotte

Music by Handel, arr. John Pitts

Duet or Solo The tune is written in the top part all the way through, so can be played solo. When played as a duet, notice that the music for the 2nd part often copies the 1st, and has lots of interest.

The Teacher's Book has some information about the **gavotte**.

Manx Lullaby

Traditional, arr. John Pitts

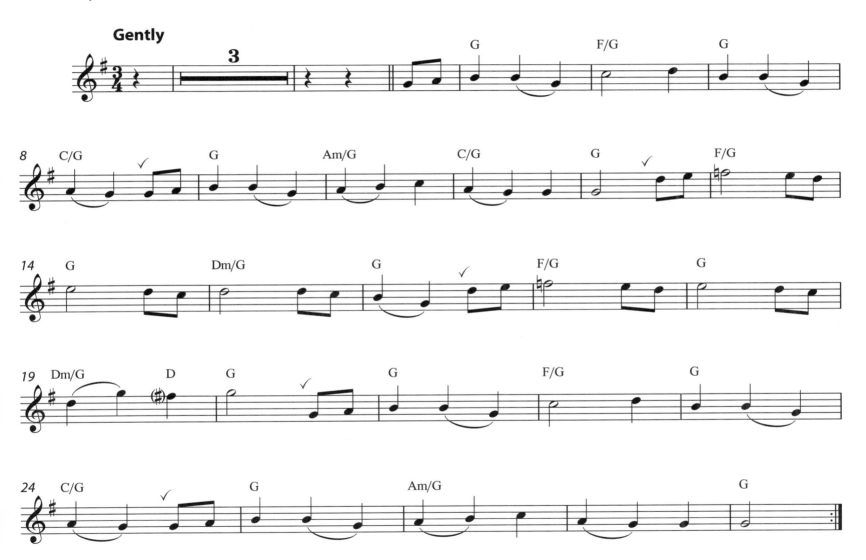

Polonaise (Polish Dance)

Traditional, arr. John Pitts

The **Polonaise** is a Polish dance that developed from courtly ceremonies in the late 16th century. It was later adopted for the ballroom and was also used for instrumental music by various composers. In the 19th century, Chopin used the Polonaise a lot in his piano music and made it a symbol of Polish patriotism.

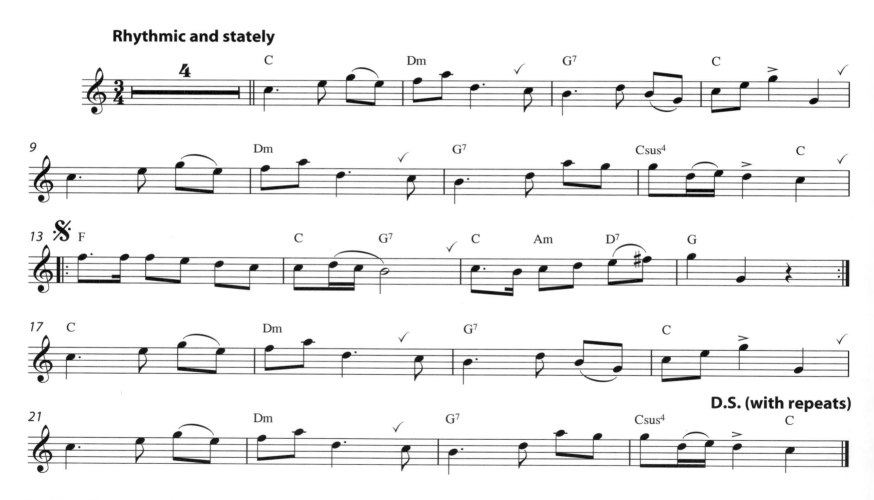

Menuetto

Composed by Wolfgang Amadeus Mozart, arr. John Pitts

Duet or Solo The main tune is in the top part throughout, so can be played solo. Although the 2nd part is optional, it has plenty of interest.

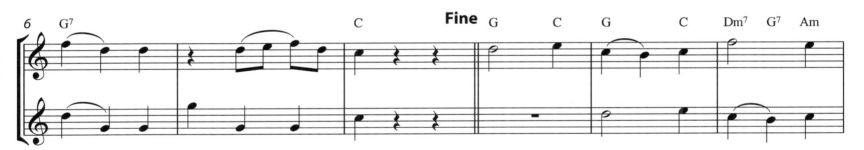

Boogie Blues

Music by John Pitts

Duet or Solo The tune is written in the top part throughout, so can be played solo. The optional 2nd part is just as interesting as it uses the same rhythms.

Steady swing, not too fast

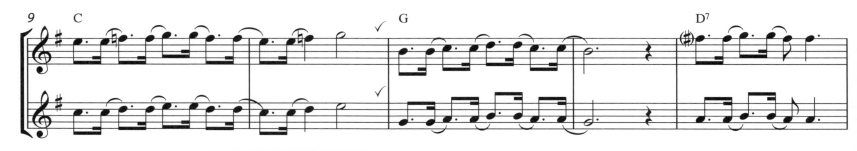

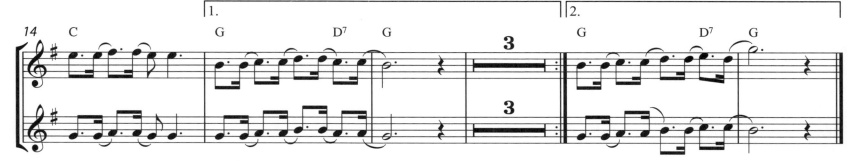

Panis Angelicus

Composed by César Franck, arr. John Pitts

Duet or Solo From [A] there is an optional 2nd part. See page 23 for details.

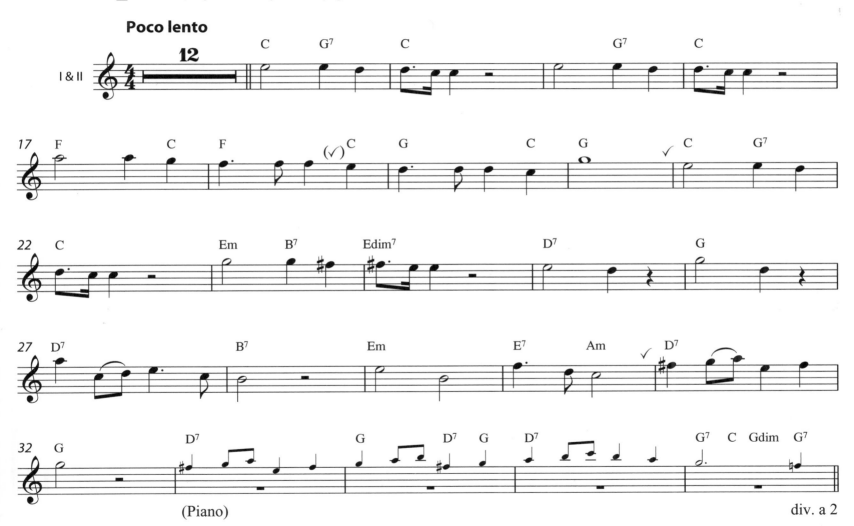

(Piano)

div. a 2

A

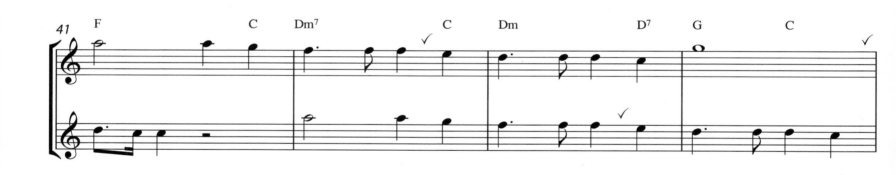

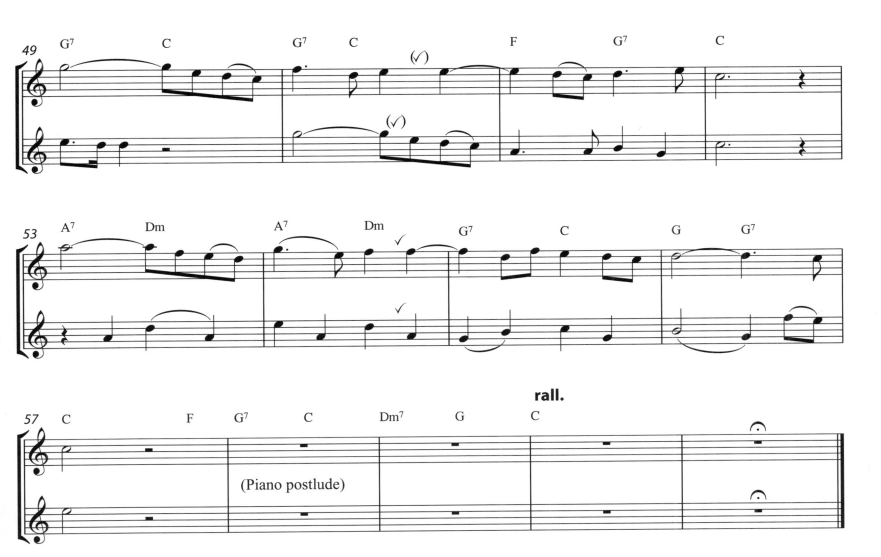

This piece was originally a song, sometimes performed in church.

From A there is an optional 2nd part. When parts I and II divide, see how both recorders play the same tune. But Recorder II begins one bar later, rather like an echo. When this happens, we call the music a **canon**.

Zinga-Za Samba (Brazilian)

Traditional, arr. John Pitts

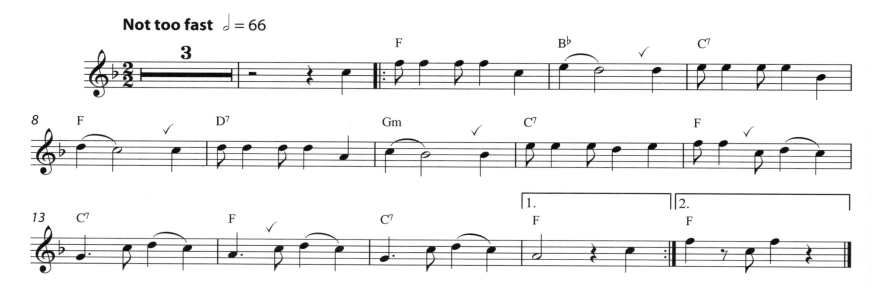

The **samba** is a Brazilian dance with a basic two beats in each bar, strongly syncopated and written in a major key. Many other Latin-American dances such as the tango are often written in a minor key.

The rhythm patterns are in two-bar phrases. A special rhythmic feature is the anticipation of the first beat of the second bar of a two-bar pattern, so this beat comes before the end of the previous bar and is tied over. You can hear this clearly at the beginning of the accompaniment, and it continues all through the accompaniment.

Get two friends to join in and play the rhythm patterns given below. Start by counting in four. Later you should count two slow beats per bar.

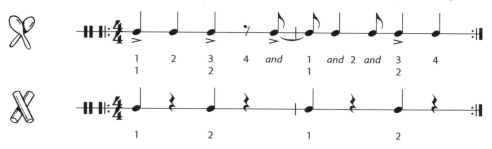

Star Of County Down (Irish)

Traditional, arr. John Pitts

Fear No Danger

Music by Henry Purcell, arr. John Pitts

Duet or Solo The main tune is in the top part, so can be played solo. See how the optional 2nd part mirrors the shape and rhythm of the 1st part.

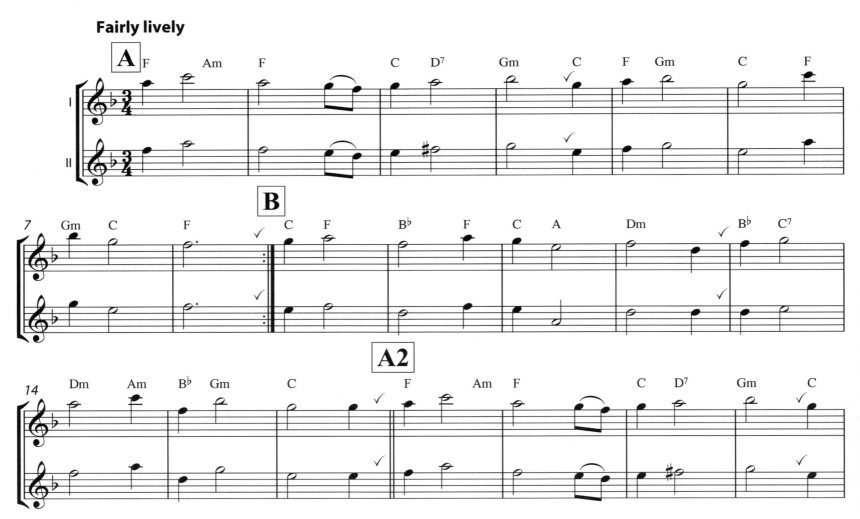

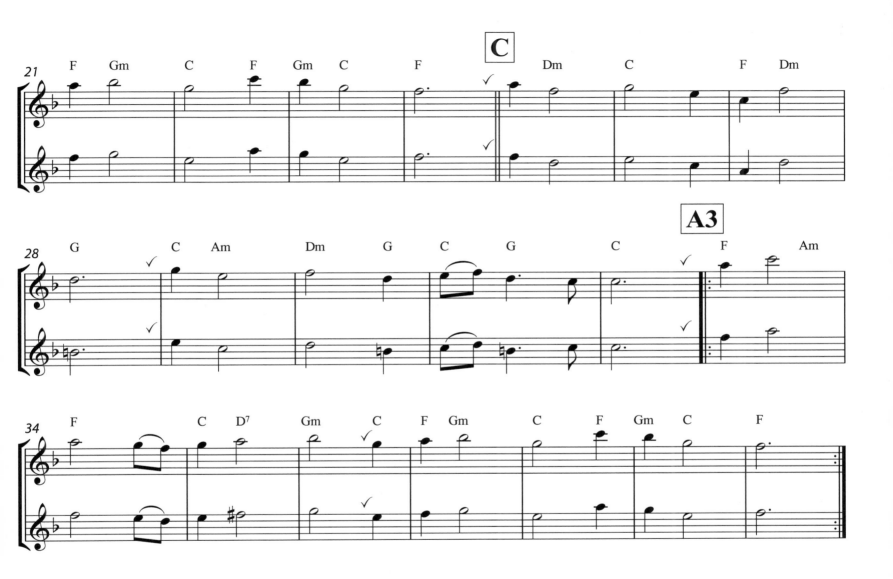

This piece is a vocal duet from Purcell's opera *Dido And Aeneas*, written in London in 1689. This particular duet uses a musical form called a **rondo**. The first tune **A** returns twice later on at **A2** and **A3**. Two contrasting passages called 'episodes' (tunes **B** and **C**) separate the returns of the main tune **A**. So a rondo can be described as an **A B A C A** form.

Little David, Play On Your Harp

(Spiritual)

Traditional, arr. John Pitts

There's some information about **spirituals** in the Teacher's Book.

To A Wild Rose

Composed by Edward MacDowell, arr. John Pitts

Las Heras Beguine

Music by John Pitts

Duet or Solo The main tune is in the top part, so can be played solo. Although the 2nd part is optional, it has just as much interest as the 1st part.

*2 = alternative fingering

The **beguine** is a Latin-American foxtrot dance. The melody is usually fairly smooth and regular, with the characteristic beguine rhythms played in the accompaniment. A simple foxtrot bass is combined with an off-beat eighth-note (quaver) rhythm. An accented second eighth-note in each bar helps to give the dance its particular character.

Two people can combine to play this beguine accompaniment.

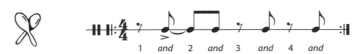

1 and 2 and 3 and 4 and

31

Peacherine Rag

Music by Scott Joplin, arr. John Pitts

* Note B is an optional alternative.

Don't Cry For Me Argentina from 'Evita'

Music by Andrew Lloyd Webber & Lyrics by Tim Rice, arr. John Pitts

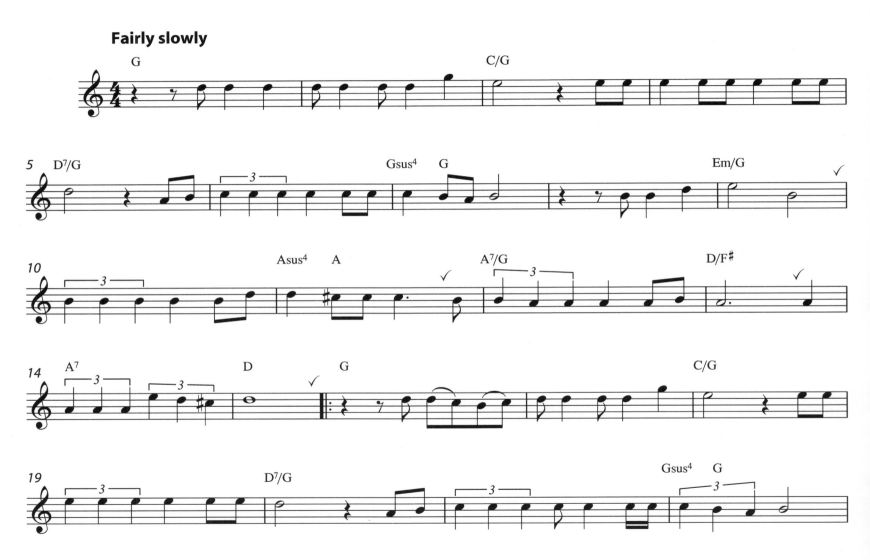

Habañera from 'Carmen'

Composed by Georges Bizet, arr. John Pitts

CD Edition: On the CD track, when you play the pause note in bar 43, listen for the tambourine roll that joins in, ending with a crash. You should move on to play the triplet after the tambourine crash.

Allegretto

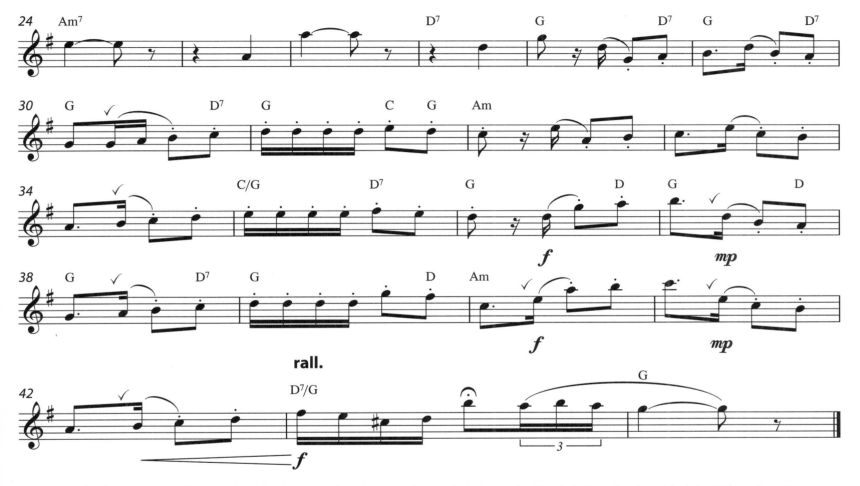

In Georges Bizet's 1875 opera *Carmen*, the title character sings the now famous habañera aria. The habañera developed in late 19th-century Havana, capital city of Cuba, from where it took its name. Another famous habañera is *La Paloma* by the Spanish composer Sebastián Yradier. The habañera influenced other Latin-American forms, such as the tango.

The distinguishing musical feature of the habañera is its short, repeating $\frac{2}{4}$ rhythmic figure in the bass-line. You can hear this very clearly in the introduction to Bizet's *Habañera*, and it continues in every single bar!

Can you see the same rhythm used anywhere in the melody?

Beauty And The Beast

from Walt Disney Pictures' 'Beauty And The Beast'

Music by Alan Menken & Words by Howard Ashman, arr. John Pitts

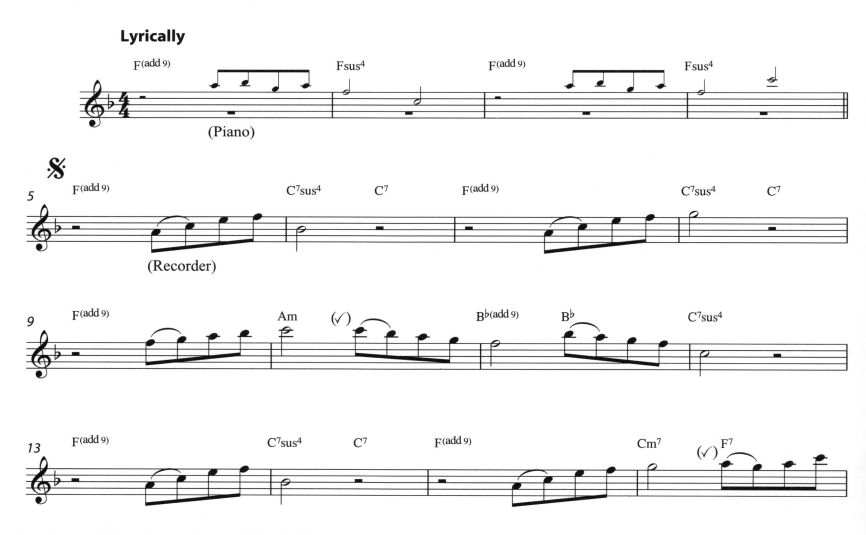

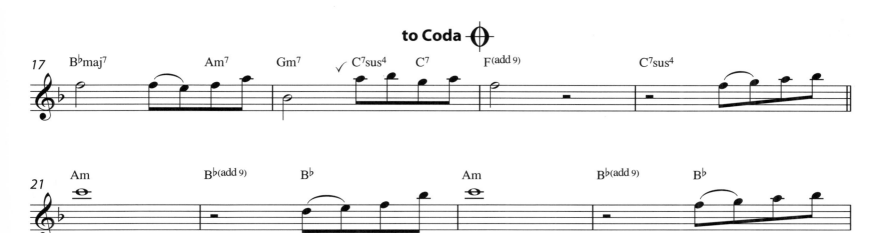

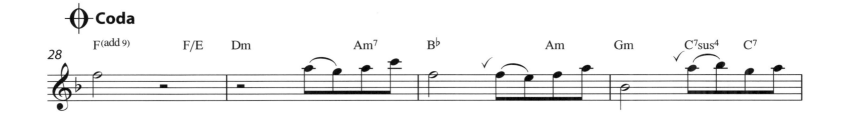

Rondeau

Music by Henry Purcell, arr. John Pitts

Henry Purcell (1659–1695) became organist at Westminster Abbey, London, at the age of just 20! His choral, instrumental and harpsichord music includes many famous pieces. His theatre music includes the first proper English opera, *Dido and Aeneas*, as well as semi-operas such as *The Fairy Queen*, from which the **Rondeau** is taken.

She Moved Through The Fair (Irish)

Traditional, arr. John Pitts

The traditional tune of this Irish song has an unusual sound because it uses the **Mixolydian mode**, a different type of scale that was used in early times. The well-known English folksong *Scarborough Fair* also uses a mode, a slightly different one called the **Dorian mode**.

The Irish folksong *Star Of County Down* (see page 25) used the **Pentatonic scale**, a special five-note scale. Some Scottish folksongs, e.g. *Over The Sea To Skye*, use the pentatonic scale. Two spirituals that use the pentatonic scale are *Swing Low, Sweet Chariot* and *Little David, Play On Your Harp*. Both these tunes are used in this book.

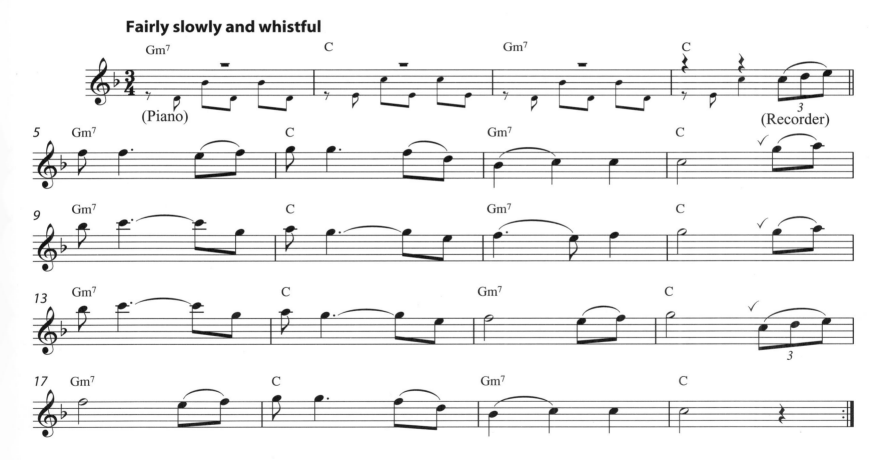

Cameron's Ragtime

Composed by John Pitts

El Choclo (Argentinian)

Music by Angel Villoldo, arr. John Pitts

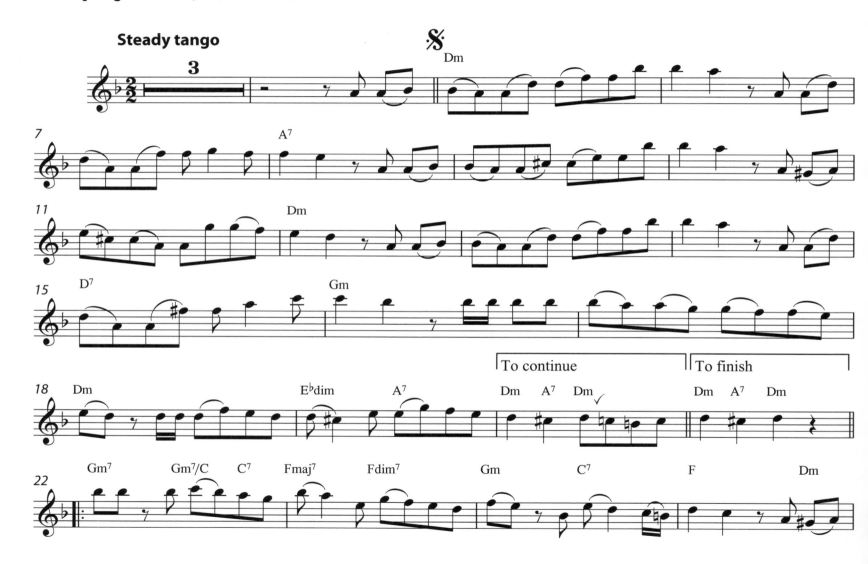

The **tango** is a Latin-American dance from Argentina, with a catchy rhythm. It began about 1900 in Buenos Aires, the capital city. In about 1915 the tango became popular in Europe as a ballroom dance. Later it was used by many composers as an independent instrumental piece.

The music has two slow beats in each bar and a dotted rhythm in the bass. To help less experienced players we often write the music in $\frac{4}{4}$ time, and both the previous tangos in this book are written in $\frac{4}{4}$ time.

The music here for *El Choclo* is in $\frac{2}{2}$ time.

No Matter What from 'Whistle Down The Wind'

Music by Andrew Lloyd Webber & Lyrics by Jim Steinman, arr. John Pitts

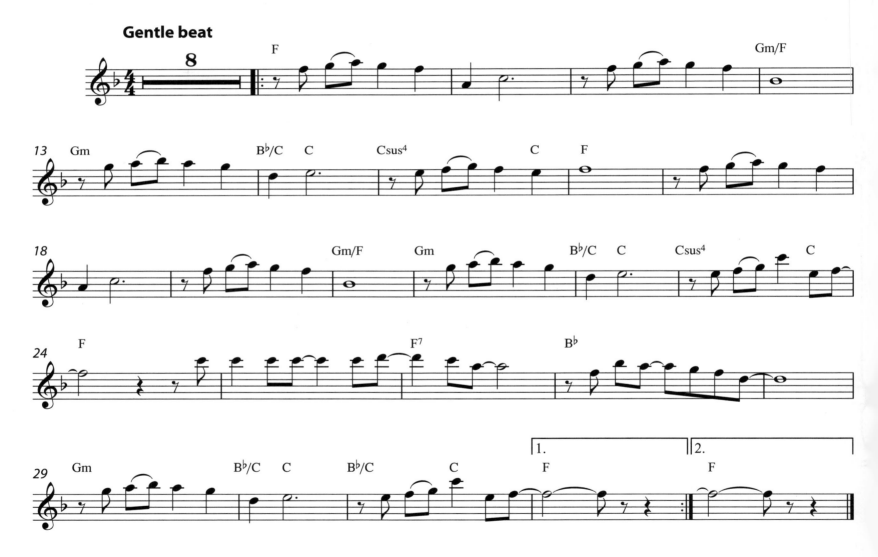

123456789

Fingering Chart
English (Baroque) Fingered Recorders

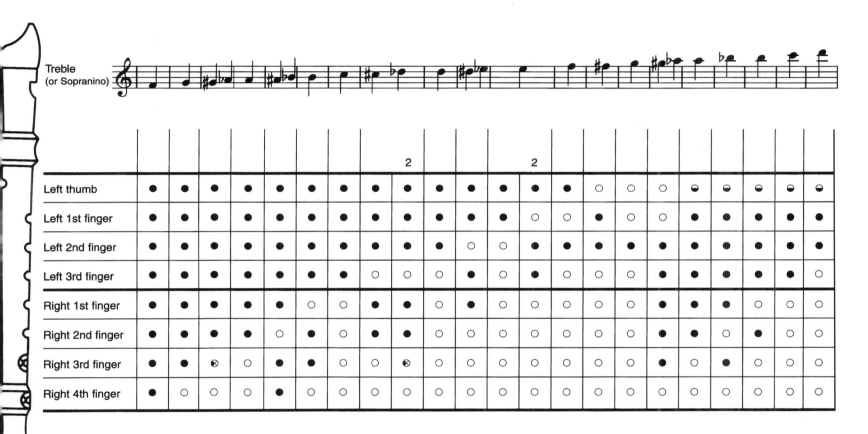

○ Open hole

● Closed hole

◙ Double hole, one closed

⊖ Partly closed hole

2 Alternative fingering

CD Track Listing

1. Tuning note (C)
2. On My Own (from 'Les Misérables')*
3. O Waly Waly
4. La Jesucita
5. Tango Chacabuco
6. Rigaudon (Chédeville)
7. Can You Feel The Love Tonight?
8. Swing Low, Sweet Chariot
9. Kalinka
10. Cascadura Beguine
11. Tango Las Plumas
12. Gavotte
13. Manx Lullaby
14. Polonaise
15. Menuetto
16. Boogie Blues
17. Panis Angelicus
18. Zinga-Za Samba
19. Star Of County Down
20. Fear No Danger
21. Little David, Play On Your Harp
22. To A Wild Rose*
23. Las Heras Beguine
24. Peacherine Rag*
25. Don't Cry For Me Argentina
26. Habañera*
27. Beauty And The Beast*
28. Rondeau
29. She Moved Through The Fair
30. Cameron's Ragtime*
31. El Choclo*
32. No Matter What*
33. On My Own (without melody)
34. To A Wild Rose (without melody)
35. Peacherine Rag (without melody)
36. Habañera (without melody)
37. Beauty And The Beast (without melody)
38. Cameron's Ragtime (without melody)
39. El Choclo (without melody)
40. No Matter What (without melody)

Track 7: (Rice/John) Warner/Chappell Artemis Music

Track 25: (Lloyd Webber/Rice) Evita Music Limited

Tracks 2 & 33: (Schönberg/Boublil/Natel) Alain Boublil Overseas Limited/SACEM

Tracks 27 & 37: (Menken/Ashman) Warner/Chappell Artemis Music

Tracks 32 & 40: (Lloyd Webber/Steinman) The Really Useful Group Limited/Universal Music Publishing Limited

All other tracks: Chester Music Limited

* For more confident players there are extra tracks for eight of the pieces.
   In these, the same accompaniment is played without the melody.

To remove your CD from the plastic sleeve,
lift the small lip to break the perforations.
Replace the disc after use for convenient storage.